NATIONAL GEOGRAPHIC KiDS

Animals

The Wild Arctic

The Rocky Mountains

British Woodland

North America

Europe

Asia

The Sahara

Africa

The Amazon Rainforest

South America

Oceania

The Serengeti Plains

The Australian Bush

Antarctica

Find it! Explore it!

The Amazon
RAINFOREST

The Amazon Rainforest is the largest tropical rainforest in the world. It is found in nine different countries in South America. It is filled with all kinds of trees, plants and wildlife.

1 Green anaconda

2 Tapirs

3 Sloths

4 Jaguars

Find it!

DID YOU KNOW?

The rainforest has many deadly creatures such as piranhas and venomous snakes.

5 Monkeys

6 Toucans

7 Leafcutter ants

8 Tree frogs

RED-EYED TREE FROG

Red-eyed tree frogs are famous creatures of the rainforest. They sleep during the day, underneath leaves. If they are disturbed, the frogs flash their huge red eyes and reveal their brightly coloured feet and sides. This surprises predators giving the tree frog time to get away.

LET'S GO!

Would you prefer to sleep at night, or during the day like a tree frog?

LET'S GO!

Look out for the magnifying glass hidden throughout the book. Collect the letters and unscramble them to spell an animal. Check your answer on page 47.

LEAFCUTTER ANTS march with chunks of leaves in their jaws. These pieces are carried back to the nest and fed to a fungus, which the ants' larvae then eat. The ants and fungus can't live without each other.

MACAW

Macaws have brightly coloured feathers. They have large, powerful beaks that are great for cracking nuts and seeds. Their dry tongues have a bone inside that is used for tapping into fruits.

TOUCAN

A toucan's large, colourful bill can grow to around 15 cm in length. It is made of keratin – the same material that your fingernails are made from.

SQUIRREL MONKEY

To clean themselves, squirrel monkeys wee on their hands and then rub it over other parts of their body!

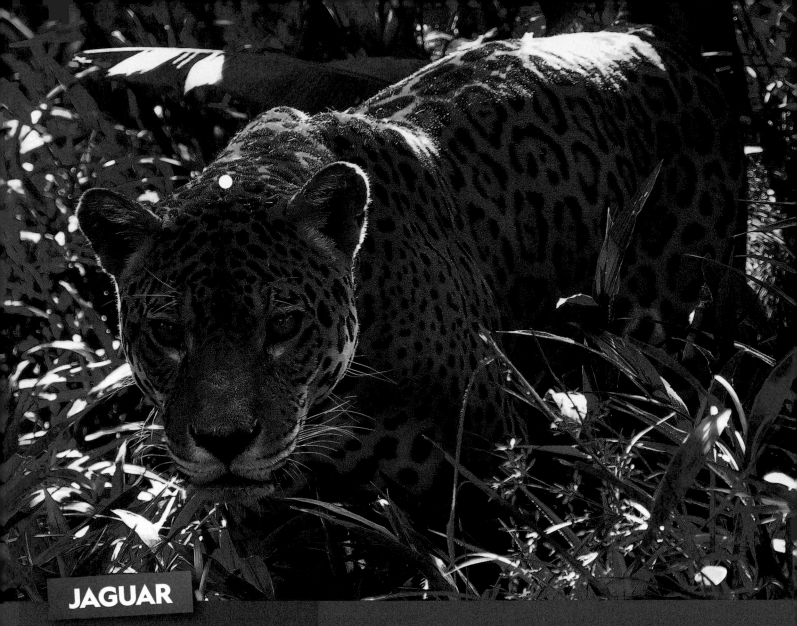

JAGUAR

Jaguars are the third-largest big cat after tigers and lions. Jaguars look a bit like leopards but their spot patterns are a little different – they often have a dot in the middle.

Can you think of any other spotted animals?

GREEN IGUANAS are fast reptiles. They have powerful jaws, razor-sharp teeth and pointed tails. If caught by a predator, the iguanas can detach their tail and grow another!

SLOTH

Sloths are the world's slowest mammal. Their slow movement and the hot rainforest air means algae grows on their furry coat. The greenish colour is useful for camouflage.

LET'S GO!

Sloths like to hang on branches. What other animals can you think of that swing on trees?

TAPIR

Tapirs look like a pig with a short trunk. However, they are actually more closely related to horses and rhinoceroses. Tapirs love water and often take a dip to cool off.

GREEN ANACONDA

Green anacondas are the world's heaviest snake – they can grow as long as a minibus. They reach their huge size by eating wild pigs, birds, and even jaguars!

The wild
ARCTIC

The Arctic is as far north as you can go! It is one of the coldest places on the planet. Even though it's chilly, there are plenty of animals that call it home!

1 Narwhal

2 Orcas

3 Walruses

4 Polar bears

In the Arctic, temperatures can drop as low as -70°C

Find it!

5 Arctic foxes

6 Reindeer

7 Seals

8 Snowy owls

REINDEER

Reindeer are also known as caribou. Unlike most types of deer, both male and female reindeer grow large antlers. They have specially designed noses that heat up the icy cold air before they breathe it in.

LET'S GO!

Next time it is cold outside, take a massive, deep breath. Can you see why reindeer need self-heating nostrils?!

LET'S GO!

Can you think of more animals that like to eat fish?

PUFFINS are seabirds that nest on cliff faces. They dive into the water to catch fish to eat. They are known for their colourful beaks, which often carry up to 12 fish at once.

Explore it!

SNOWY OWL

Snowy owls have very thick layers of feathers. They also look like they have fluffy slippers. This is thanks to the extra feathers around their legs and feet that keep them warm.

BEARDED SEAL

Bearded seals are the largest type of seal in the Arctic – they weigh around the same as a grand piano! Bearded seals get their name because of their long whiskers that look like a beard.

ARCTIC FOX

Arctic foxes have brown coats in the summer and white coats in the winter. This makes for great camouflage whatever the season.

POLAR BEAR

Polar bears are the largest carnivorous (meat-eating) land mammals on the planet. Their fur appears white, which helps to keep them camouflaged in the snow and ice. Their skin is black to help soak in the sun's rays and keep them warm.

NARWHALS look like unicorns of the sea thanks to the single horn on the front of their head. But these 'horns' are actually more like teeth and are very sensitive!

LET'S GO!

Would you rather be a unicorn or a narwhal?

WALRUS

Walruses are massive! They can be as long and as heavy as a car! Walruses have tusks that they use to pull themselves out of the water and to fight other walruses.

ORCA

Orcas are enormous – they are almost the same length as a bus! They are also very intelligent mammals. They work in packs and have been known to make waves to knock prey into the sea that can then be hunted.

LET'S GO!

Orcas have their own language. Can you make up your own language using sounds?

British
WOODLAND

Ancient woodland usually has large trees that have been growing for hundreds of years. Some woodlands look spooky with their curling branches. They are the perfect places for wildlife to hide!

1 Tawny owl

 **2 Pheasants**

3 Badgers

 **4 Hedgehogs**

Find it!

DID YOU KNOW?

Some areas of British woodland are over 400 years old!

5 Squirrels

6 Foxes

7 Rabbits

8 Woodpeckers

FOX

Foxes are ginger mammals that look like a cross between a cat and a dog. They are fast and active animals. Foxes are good hunters, too. They like to hunt rabbits, rodents and birds but also eat berries.

GREY SQUIRREL

Grey squirrels are playful creatures with bushy tails. They live in trees. Their nest is called a 'drey' and they protect it by barking and wiggling their tails when they are scared.

WOODPECKER

Woodpeckers are brightly coloured birds. Some of them make a fast pecking sound by tapping on tree trunks.

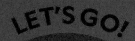

LET'S GO!

Woodpeckers have very long tongues – is your tongue long enough to touch your nose?

RABBIT

Rabbits are animals with long ears that live in underground burrows called 'warrens'. When they are happy, they make a big jump, twisting and kicking in the air – this is called a 'binky' jump!

RED SQUIRRELS are much smaller than grey squirrels and are an endangered species.

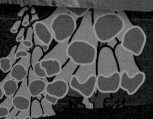

LET'S GO!

Next time you hear a bird singing, try to copy its call (and see if it responds to you).

TAWNY OWL

Like most owls, tawny owls are nocturnal. This means that they sleep during the day and are awake at night.

LET'S GO!

Can you curl into a ball like a hedgehog? See how small you can make yourself.

HEDGEHOGS are spikey little creatures that rustle through the undergrowth looking for juicy slugs to eat. They can have between 5,000 and 7,000 spikes on their back depending on their size.

BADGER

Badgers are mammals that like to eat whatever they can find. They live in large burrows called 'sets'. Badgers look after their homes very carefully – they make sure they go to the toilet outside.

PHEASANT

Pheasants are medium sized birds. Male pheasants (right) are very brightly coloured. The females are much less flashy.

ROE DEER

Roe deer have a light brown coat. They have big black eyes and noses. The males have small antlers with three points to them. Deer are very athletic and can jump as high as 1.5 m – that's right over your head!

(K)

The SAHARA

The Sahara in Africa is one of the largest deserts in the world! It is also one of the world's hottest places and has been known to reach temperatures over 50 °C!

1 Camel

2 Fennec foxes

3 Barbary sheep

4 Desert hares

Find it!

DID YOU KNOW?

The Sahara is almost as big as the USA!

5 Gazelles **6 Cobras** **7 Scorpions** **8 Jerboas**

LET'S GO!

Would you prefer to run really fast or jump really high?

JERBOA

Jerboas look like mice on stilts! They come out at night and can move very fast. Jerboas jump to escape preadtors.

COBRA

Cobras have a hood around their head that make them easy to recognise. There are many types of cobra that live in the Sahara and all of them are venomous!

LET'S GO!

Can you scurry like a scorpion to the other side of the room?

GAZELLE

Gazelles look a bit like deer, but they have curved, ringed-horns instead of antlers.

SCORPION

Scorpions are closely related to spiders. They have a large stinging tail which comes up over their body. They also have large pincers like crabs.

23

CAMEL

Camels are large desert animals that look like llamas with huge humps on their back. Their humps are used to store fat. The fat gives camels energy for their treks across the hot desert when there isn't much food or water.

LET'S GO!

What's your favourite desert animal and why?

FENNEC FOX

Fennec foxes are some of the smallest foxes around, with some of the biggest ears! Their ears aren't just big to help them hear; they help them to cool down, too.

BARBARY SHEEP

Barbary sheep are great at jumping. They can leap 2 metres high, which is higher than the height of most adult humans.

CAPE HARE

Cape hares have large eyes, good eyesight and pointy ears. These hares sometimes eat their own droppings!

The Rocky
MOUNTAINS

The Rocky Mountains run through Canada and the USA. The mountains have lots of different types of weather, which means many different kinds of animals live there.

1 Lynx

2 Mountain lions

3 Coyotes

4 Moose

DID YOU KNOW?

The Rocky Mountains were made by big plates of earth sliding under each other and pushing the mountains up to the sky.

5 Grizzly bears

6 Beavers

7 Bighorn sheep

8 Chipmunks

BEAVER

Beavers are furry mammals. They have big teeth for chomping through trees and bark. They have flat tails that help them swim but can also be slapped against the water to signal danger!

COYOTE

Coyotes are like small wolves that like to hunt at night. They have great eyesight and a good sense of smell. They have also been known to chase prey for miles, before eventually hunting it down.

Can you howl like a coyote? Give it a try!

BIGHORN SHEEP

Bighorn sheep live on the slopes of the Rocky Mountains. They have huge curled horns. Bighorn sheep in the Rockies grow much bigger than bighorn sheep that live in other places.

GRIZZLY BEAR

Grizzly bears are very large meat-eating mammals. They have a big hump on their back that is a muscle they use for digging.

LET'S GO

Can you puff up your cheeks like a chipmunk?

CHIPMUNK

Chipmunks are like stripey squirrels with very stretchy cheeks! They hibernate in the winter but wake up every now and again for a nutty snack.

BLACK BEAR

Black bears come in many colours such as black, red and blond. When they hibernate during the winter, they do not eat, drink or go to the toilet.

MOUNTAIN LION

Mountain lions and cougars are the same animal. They are big cats that can move quickly and can leap long distances!

LYNX

Lynxes are medium-sized cats with fluffy tips on the end of their ears. They have short tails and their back legs are longer than their front legs. This helps them to pounce!

MOOSE

Moose are the biggest species of deer in the world. All moose have a pouch of skin called a 'bell' that hangs from their neck. The males have enormous antlers.

LET'S GO!

Would you rather have horns or antlers?

RACOON

Racoons have some of the most skillful hands in the animal kingdom! Their name means 'animal that scratches with its hands' and they are known for gathering food with their human-like fingers.

The Australian BUSH

The Australian bush is a name given to wooded natural areas of Australia. Hardly any people live in the Australian bush, but plenty of animals do!

1 Platypus

2 Wombats

3 Emus

4 Echidnas

Find it!

33

KANGAROO

Kangaroos are the largest marsupials in the world. Marsupial animals carry their babies in a pouch!

LET'S GO!

If you had your own pouch, what would you keep in it and why?

REDBACK SPIDERS are closely related to black widow spiders and are very venomous. They usually eat insects and other spiders but have been known to eat larger animals such as lizards.

LET'S GO!

If you could have a coloured back, what colour would you make it?

Explore it!

FRILLED LIZARD

Frilled lizards have big frills around their necks. The frills are used to scare away predators. They hiss and run as well if they need to!

DINGO

Dingoes are wild dogs with large wedge-shaped heads. They rarely bark, preferring to howl or chatter instead.

PLATYPUS

Platypuses are strange looking animals. They have a bill and webbed feet like a duck. They have a tail like a beaver and a body similar to an otter.

KOALA

Koalas are small grey marsupials that spend most of their time sleeping. They sleep for more than 18 hours a day! When they aren't sleeping they are eating lots of eucalyptus leaves.

KOOKABURAS are the largest member of the kingfisher family. They have a large head and beak. They are also known for their call that sounds like they are giggling!

LET'S GO!

How long can you laugh for? Try it with a friend or your family, you might make each other laugh too!

ECHIDNA

Echidnas look like a cross between a hedgehog and an anteater. They are amazing because they are one of only two mammals in the world that lay eggs! The other is the platypus.

LET'S GO!

Which Australian bush animal is your favourite and why?

EMU

Emus are the second tallest bird in the world, after the ostrich. They have soft fluffy feathers and long, powerful legs. Emus can't fly but they can run very fast!

WOMBAT

Wombats are great at digging thanks to their claws and barrel-shaped bodies. Female wombats have pouches that face backwards so that they can dig without getting soil in it.

The Serengeti
PLAINS

The Serengeti plains are in Tanzania, Africa. They contain many habitats, such as forests, swamps and grasslands. These places are home to lots of different types of animals.

1 Hippopotamus

2 Rhinoceros

3 Leopards

4 Elephants

DID YOU KNOW?

Over two million animals take part in a migration (movement to a new area) at the Serengeti plains.

5 Giraffes

6 Buffalos

7 Lions

8 Zebras

ZEBRA

Zebras are known for their stripey pattern. Each zebra's pattern is unique. This means no two zebras are the same.

LET'S GO!

Which Serengeti animal would you most like to see in the wild?

LION

Lions are known as the kings of the animal world. They have powerful bodies and males have bushy manes. Lions live in groups called a 'pride'.

BUFFALO

Buffalos are amazingly strong. They can live in herds that are made up of more than 1,000 buffalos!

LET'S GO!

What animal feature would you like to have? Powerful like a lion? Tall like a giraffe? Or strong like a buffalo?

GIRAFFE

Giraffes are the tallest animals in the world! Thanks to their extremely long necks, they can grow to be well over 5 metres! That's as high as three tall humans standing on top of each other!

LET'S GO!

What do you like most about elephants?

ELEPHANT

Elephants are the biggest land animals in the world. They also have brilliant memories and they know and remember each member of their herd. Their big brains are capable of remembering and recognising over 30 different elephants!

CHEETAHS are the fastest land animals and the fastest runners in the world. They also have great balance. This is how their heads stay so still when they run at speeds of over 90 km/h!

LEOPARD

Leopards are powerful, clever big cats. They often pull their prey onto branches of trees so they can eat in peace!

LET'S GO!

If you were an animal, would you rather have spots or stripes?

RHINOCEROS

Rhinoceroses are very strong and very fast. They have sharp horns on their noses. They are the second largest land animal and have a strong sense of smell.

HIPPOPOTAMUS

Hippopotamuses are dangerous animals. They are strong, aggressive and have very big teeth. Their bite is so powerful that it can snap a canoe in half.

SOLUTIONS

The Amazon Rainforest

The Wild Arctic

British Woodland

The Sahara

The Rocky Mountains

The Australian Bush

Magnifying glass game

Monkey

Published by Collins
An imprint of HarperCollins Publishers
Westerhill Road
Bishopbriggs
Glasgow G64 2QT
www.harpercollins.co.uk

HarperCollins Publishers
1st Floor, Watermarque Building, Ringsend Road, Dublin 4, Ireland

In association with National Geographic Partners, LLC

First published 2021

ISBN 978-0-00-842191-5

10 9 8 7 6 5 4 3 2

A catalogue record for this book is available from the British Library

Printed in Glasgow by Bell & Bain Ltd.

If you would like to comment on any aspect of this book,
please contact us at the above address or online.
natgeokidsbooks.co.uk
collins.reference@harpercollins.co.uk

Paper from responsible sources.

Acknowledgements

Illustrations by Steve Evans
Images © Shutterstock.com